Penmanship
MASTERY I

Fourth Edition

Phyllis Rand *Ed. D.*

abeka.
Pensacola, FL 32523-9100
an affiliate of PENSACOLA CHRISTIAN COLLEGE®

☙ abeka.

Penmanship Program

Writing with Phonics K4

Writing with Phonics K5

Writing with Phonics 1

Writing with Phonics 2

Cursive Writing Skillbook (3)

Penmanship Mastery I (4)

Penmanship Mastery II (5)

Creative Writing (6)

◆ ◆ ◆

Penmanship Teaching Aids

Penmanship Mastery I
Fourth Edition

Staff Credits
Editor: Corinne Sawtelle
Designer: Shawn Thayer

Cataloging Data
Rand, Phyllis
          Penmanship mastery I / Phyllis Rand—4th ed.
     145 p. : col. ill. ; 28 cm.
    1. Penmanship—Study and teaching (Elementary) I. Phyllis Rand. II. Abeka Book, Inc.
III. Title: Penmanship mastery one.

Library of Congress: Z43 .R5 2008
Dewey System: 372.63

Photo credits are listed left to right, top to bottom on the page. CB for Corbis Corporation, CC for Corel Corporation.

Photo Credits: 14–Digital Vision; 20–CB; 26–Scott Camazine/Photo Researchers, Inc.; 31–CC; 33–Jupiterimages; 35–Schuster Catalog/SuperStock; 37–flag CB; 39–Stockbyte; 40–Ruth Ann Chappell; 41–CB; 42–map image from Mountain High Maps copyright ©1997 Digital Wisdom, Inc.; 43–Richard Heinzen/SuperStock; 46–CC; 47–CB; 48–Schuster/SuperStock; 49–skodonnell/istockphoto.com; 52, 53–CC; 56–Ariel Skelley/CORBIS; 58–4x5 Coll-Francisco Cruz/SuperStock; 59–map image from Mountain High Maps copyright ©1997 Digital Wisdom, Inc.; 60–Digital Vision; 64–CC; 66–Pamela Moore/istockphoto.com; 71–Yuri/istockphoto.com; 74–CB; 75–Jupiterimages; 82–TPS UK OWNED/SuperStock; 87–right CB; 89, 96, 103–CB; 110–4x5 Coll-PR Productions 1991/SuperStock; 112–CC; 113–Stefan Janeschitz/istockphoto.com; 115–CB; 116, 117–Jupiterimages; 119–CB; 121–CC, CB.

To Teachers and Parents

Penmanship Mastery I continues the teaching and practice of the penmanship skills taught in Abeka *Writing with Phonics K–2* books and *Cursive Writing Skillbook* for grade 3. It includes all the material needed for fourth grade penmanship. Teaching suggestions, journal entry topics, and sentence dictation are included in the Language Arts 4 Curriculum.

Penmanship Mastery I

- is carefully correlated with the rest of the Abeka language arts program for fourth grade. Many of the penmanship exercises are correlated with the students' spelling and language lessons.

- provides *daily* instruction and practice for penmanship excellence. Students practice correct formation, spacing, letter size, slant, and proportion, as well as overall neatness and good appearance.

- is primarily a penmanship practice workbook, but it also gives students opportunity to enjoy interesting and challenging games and think about many of the character traits that are taught in their spelling lessons.

Please note these useful features of *Penmanship Mastery I*:

1. There is one page of work that is to be written on notebook paper for each class day. Samples may be traced on the printed page, but all writing is done on notebook paper.

2. The lessons are 20 minutes long. Since the goal is to provide penmanship practice, students are encouraged to concentrate on their writing skills.

3. Fourth grade students are taught to write capital letters that are ¾-space high, and most lowercase letters are proportionately smaller. The lines in *Penmanship Mastery I* are the same size as regular wide-ruled notebook paper. The blue dotted lines at the beginning of the book serve as a reminder to the students of ¾ spacing.

4. The first 26 pages provide a concentrated review of the correct formation of individual letters.

5. After the completion of the review, each week's lessons consist of
   a. practice with difficult connections
   b. practice with that week's spelling words
   c. creative writing: "A Word to Live By" or Journal Entry
   d. penmanship test
   e. practice with sentence dictation and a creative writing activity

   Note: Selections for the tests begin on page 123 of this book. They are to be copied by the students onto notebook paper.

6. After page 26, a progress report will be included at the top of one lesson each week. The report should be filled in appropriately by the teacher as she circulates the room checking work.

Pen and Paper Positions

How to Hold Your Pen or Pencil/How to Slant Your Paper

Right-Handed Writers

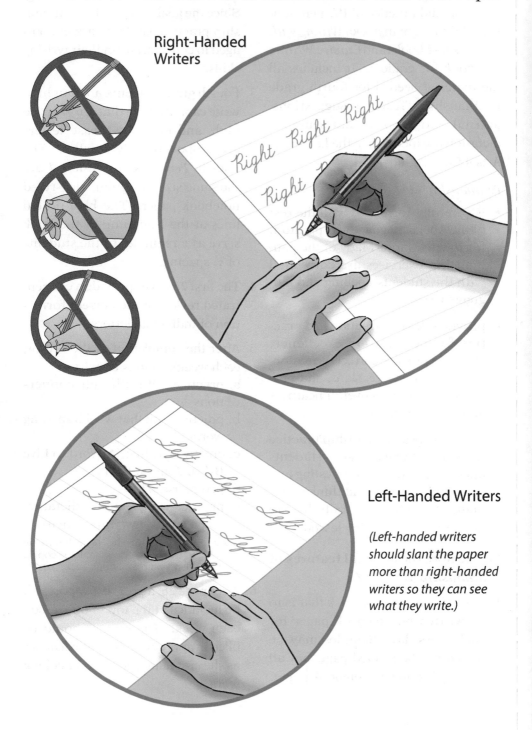

Left-Handed Writers

(Left-handed writers should slant the paper more than right-handed writers so they can see what they write.)

Cursive Formation Guide

Aa Bb Cc Dd
Ee Ff Gg Hh
Ii Jj Kk Ll
Mm Nn Oo Pp
Qq Rr Ss Tt
Uu Vv Ww Xx
Yy Zz . ? ! ,

1 2 3 4 5
6 7 8 9 10

Next pages—turn and tear out for class use.

FOCUS on Formation

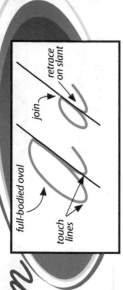

full-bodied oval

join

retrace on slant

touch lines

Warm Up

Trace each sample and write a row of each on notebook paper.

 O   ccc   A   a   American   Adam

Practice

Copy the quotation carefully on notebook paper.

One man with courage makes a majority.
—Andrew Jackson

Practice

Study the sample heading. Write a heading for your penmanship and spelling papers on notebook paper.

Name

Subject

Date

Penmanship Mastery I • Lesson 1

Trace each sample and write a row of each on notebook paper.

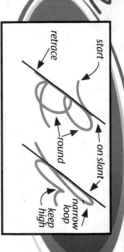

start

retrace

on slant

round

narrow loop

keep high

O U B R Boston   Bible

Copy each sentence 3 times on notebook paper.

Baseball is America's pastime.

Beth has blue bubble bath.

Thomas Edison invented the light bulb.

FOCUS on Formation

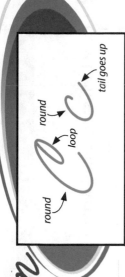

round → 𝒞 ← round

loop

tail goes up

Warm Up

Trace each sample and write a row of each on notebook paper.

𝒸𝒸𝒸   𝒞 𝒸 𝒸   Christ - city

Creative Writing

Copy each word on notebook paper; then write 2 other words that start with c beside it.

character   camping

Christmas   Calvary

cross   curious

3

Note: L 4 is a test. See p. 123.

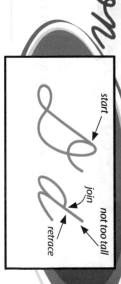

start →
not too tall
join
retrace

 Warm Up

Trace each sample and write a row of each on notebook paper:

$\mathcal{O}$ ccc $\mathcal{D}$ d   December   Daniel

 Practice

Copy the sentence 3 times on notebook paper.

Old ducks dive deeper.

Creative Writing

List some ways to be friendly to a new student in your class. Use complete sentences on notebook paper.

Smile and say, "Hello!"

FOCUS on Formation

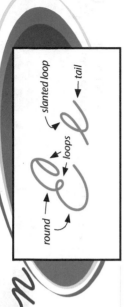

round ——→ ——← slanted loop
loops ——↗
←— tail

Trace each sample and write a row of each on notebook paper:

𝒪   eee   𝒞   e   Esther   Eve

How many color words can you think of that have *e* in them? How many number words between 1 and 12 can you think of that have *e* in them? Write as many as you can.

Try your skill at making words. The first three letters are given for you. Can you make at least one six-letter word for each one? Make as many words as you can.

n   nu   num

l   fr   fra

ur   wri   wrin

Penmanship Mastery I • Lesson 6

FOCUS on Formation

 Warm Up

Trace each sample and write a row of each on notebook paper.

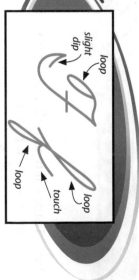

0   *O*   *U*   *F*   *f*   *Friday*   *Florida*

Practice

Copy the sentence 3 times on notebook paper.

Frank threw Fred five free throws.

Practice

Copy Spelling List 1.

Lesson 7 • *Penmanship Mastery I*

6

FOCUS on Formation

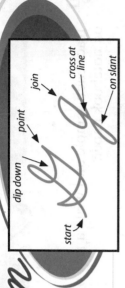

dip down point join cross at line on slant start

Warm Up

Trace each sample and write a row of each on notebook paper.

ccc G g Genesis God

Practice

Copy the following poem two times on notebook paper. Be sure to use your *best* penmanship!

**Good, better, best;
Never let it rest
Till your good is better,
And your better best.**

Good, better,

7

Penmanship Mastery I • Lesson 8
Note: L 9 is a test. See p. 123.

FOCUS on *Formation*

loop
cross
oval
retrace
on slant
round
touch line

Warm Up

Trace each sample and write a row of each on notebook paper.

All   H   h   Heaven   Heidi

Creative Writing

Write a sentence with each word on notebook paper.

church hospital

Creative Writing

List at least 10 things on notebook paper for which you are thankful.

1. *my parents*
2. _____
3. *etc.*

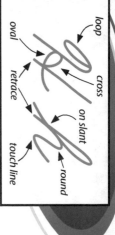

FOCUS on Formation

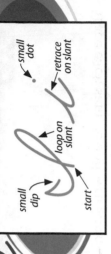

small dip →
loop on slant
start
•← small dot
retrace on slant

Trace each sample and write a row of each on notebook paper.

uu   l   i   icicle   Indian

How many words do you know that begin with *i*? Write them on notebook paper.

Put on your "Thinking Cap" and copy what you are given for each number; then write the next letter or letters in the series beside it on notebook paper. The first one is done for you.

1. x y   *x y z*
2. a ab
3. lo mo
4. jpp kpp

5. t tt
6. a c
7. o oo
8. ka la

9. q qr
10. z y
11. cde   fgh
12. bbb bb

9

FOCUS on *Formation*

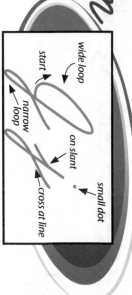

wide loop
start
on slant
small dot
narrow loop
cross at line

 Warm Up

Trace each sample and write a row of each on notebook paper.

Creative Writing

Write a sentence on notebook paper using the word *jelly*.

Practice

Copy Spelling List 2.

FOCUS on Formation

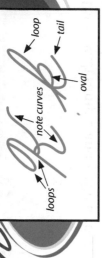

note curves

loops

loop

oval

tail

Warm Up

Trace each sample and write a row of each on notebook paper.

Ull   K   k   Kentucky   Kansas

Practice

Trace each sentence and then copy it 2 times in your best penmanship on notebook paper.

Kindness gives birth to kindness.

Keep thy tongue from evil.

Little tasks make large return.

Love is kind.

11

Penmanship Mastery I • Lesson 13

Note: L 14 is a test. See p. 123.

FOCUS on Formation

Warm Up

Trace each sample and write a row of each on notebook paper.

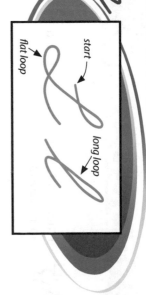

start
flat loop
long loop

Ll L l Lord Luke

tell level little

Creative Writing

You told your coach that you would be at soccer practice, but your best friend just invited you to go camping with his family. What should you do? Why? Write your answers in complete sentences on notebook paper.

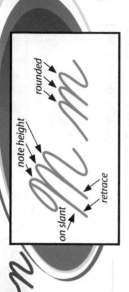

FOCUS on Formation

note height → rounded
on slant → $\mathcal{M}$ m ← retrace

Trace each sample and write a row of each on notebook paper.

mmm $\mathcal{M}$ m Matthew Mark

Write 10 sentences using words that begin with *m*.

Rewrite the following fragments on notebook paper, making them part of complete sentences.

1. on the bus

2. near the road

3. is working on his homework

4. I have always wanted to

13

Penmanship Mastery I • Lesson 16

FOCUS on Formation

loop

retrace

note height

rounded

Trace each sample and write a row of each on notebook paper.

mmm n n November Noah

Copy the tongue twister twice on notebook paper.

Nick knocks nightly.

Copy Spelling List 3 on notebook paper.

FOCUS on Formation

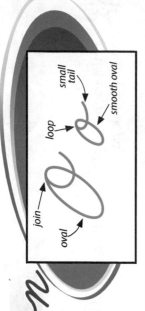

join → oval → loop → small tail → smooth oval

Trace each sample and write a row of each on notebook paper.

ccc O O o October Oregon

Trace and copy each word four times on notebook paper. Write carefully! Then use each word in a sentence.

1. ocean
2. obedience
3. others

4. office
5. Omaha
6. ordinary

Penmanship Mastery I • Lesson 18

Note: L 19 is a test. See p. 123.

15

FOCUS on Formation

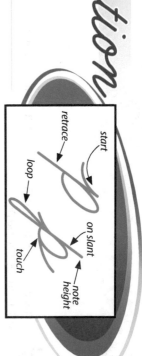

start
retrace
loop
on slant
touch
note height

 Warm Up

Trace each sample and write a row of each on notebook paper:

ccc   P   p   Peter   Paul

 Practice

In your best penmanship copy the Bible verse 3 times on notebook paper:

Providing for honest things, not only in the sight of the Lord, but also in the sight of men. —2 Corinthians 8:21

 **Practice**

There is a sentence in each jumble of letters below. When you find it, copy it on notebook paper, putting capital letters and punctuation in the right places.

sitawrotsrapidlyinseduratercolor

soundandsroundthsruggedrockthsraggedrascalban

FOCUS on Formation

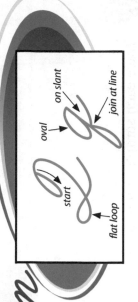

- oval
- start
- on slant
- join at line
- flat loop

Trace each sample and write a row of each on notebook paper.

Qqq   Q   q   Quebec   Queen Anne

Write 2 sentences with each word on notebook paper.

1. *quit*
2. *quick*
3. *quiz*
4. *liquid*
5. *Queen Elizabeth*
6. *Quebec*
7. *equator*
8. *quiet*

17

slant

retrace

dip down

Warm Up

Trace each sample and write a row of each on notebook paper.

rrr   R   r   Ruth   Rebekah

Practice

Copy Spelling List 4 on notebook paper.

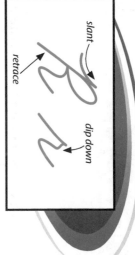

FOCUS on Formation

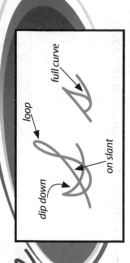

loop

dip down

on slant

full curve

 Trace each sample and write a row of each on notebook paper.

L   s   Stephen   September

 Trace and copy each quotation 2 times on notebook paper.

Sin can keep you from the Bible, and the Bible can keep you from sin.

Christ hates sin but loves the sinner.

Be swift to hear, slow to speak, slow to wrath.   James 1:19

19

Note: *L 24 is a test. See p. 124.*

loop
slight dip
note crossing height
retrace on slant

Trace each sample and write a row of each on notebook paper.

lll *I* *t* *Tennessee* *Timothy*

Copy this poem twice on notebook paper.

Thirty days hath September,
April, June, and November.
All the rest have thirty-one,
Save February, which has twenty-eight
Until Leap Year gives it twenty-nine.

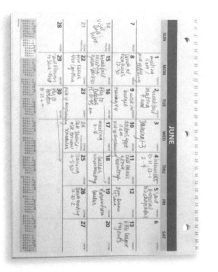

FOCUS on Formation

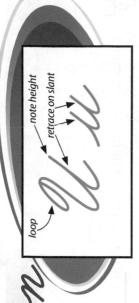

loop
note height
retrace on slant

𝒰 𝓊

Warm Up

Trace each sample and write a row of each on notebook paper.

𝓊𝓊 𝒰 𝓊 Utah United States

Creative Writing

Write 10 words that begin with *u* or contain *u* on notebook paper. Use each of the first five in a sentence.

Creative Writing

How many words can you make? The first 3 letters of each word are given to you. Can you make a word with 6 or more letters?

1. par   *particle*
2. tel
3. som
4. sta
5. han
6. ind
7. hav
8. fin

Penmanship Mastery I • Lesson 26

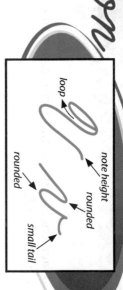

note height

loop

rounded

rounded

small tail

Warm Up

Trace each sample and write a row of each on notebook paper.

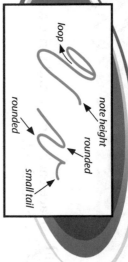

uu   *I*   *r*   *Vermont*   *Virginia*

Practice

Copy the quotation 3 times on notebook paper.

Love comforteth like sunshine after rain. —*Shakespeare*

Practice

Copy Spelling List 5 on notebook paper.

FOCUS on Formation

Penmanship Mastery I • Lesson 28

Note: L 29 is a test. See p. 124.

note height
retrace
rounded
small tail
start
point

W W w

Washington Wednesday

Warm Up

Trace each sample and write a row of each on notebook paper.

w W w

Practice

Copy this fun poem 2 times on notebook paper.

Said a boy to his teacher one day,
"Wright has not written 'rite' right, I say."

And the teacher replied
As the blunder she eyed:—

"Right—Wright, write 'rite' right,
right away!"

23

FOCUS on Formation

loop → cross goes down
cross at center
touch line → curve

Warm Up

Trace each sample and write a row of each on notebook paper.

n n n X x Xerxes X-rays

Practice

Copy the sentence carefully 3 times on notebook paper.

He who is good at making excuses is seldom good for anything else.

Creative Writing

We must first be loyal to God and to what He tells us in His Word. Name some other persons or things to which you owe your loyalty and devotion. List at least 5 on notebook paper.

1. *country*

FOCUS on Formation

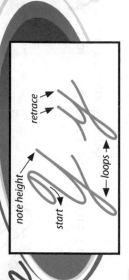

Warm Up

Trace each sample and write a row of each on notebook paper.

uu   y   y   Yellowstone   Yukon

Creative Writing

Write as many words that begin with *y* as you can on notebook paper. Use each of the first 5 in a sentence.

Creative Writing

Write as many words that end in *y* as you can on notebook paper. Use each of the first 5 in a sentence.

Trace each sample and write a row of each on notebook paper.

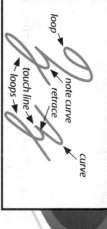

loop → ↘
note curve
retrace →
touch line → ↓
loops → ↘
curve

Copy this fun poem 2 times on notebook paper.

There Was a Bee

There was a bee
Sat on a wall
And "Buzz!" said he,
And that was all.

Copy Spelling List 6 on notebook paper.

Trace each sample and write a row of each on notebook paper.

g g g   abcdefghijklmnopqrstuvwxyz

Trace and copy each line.

Aa Bb Cc Dd Ee Ff Gg Hh Ii Jj Kk Ll Mm
Nn Oo Pp Qq Rr Ss Tt Uu Vv Ww Xx Yy Zz

Copy these number words and numbers 3 times each.

one 1   two 2   three 3   four 4   five 5   six 6
seven 7   eight 8   nine 9   ten 10

Penmanship Mastery I • Lesson 33
Note: *L 34 is a test. See p. 124.*

27

© 2008–2015 Educational Ventures, Inc. Not to be reproduced.

Trace each sample and write a row of each on notebook paper.

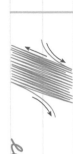

Do you see at least six things wrong in this picture? Make a list on notebook paper, using complete sentences.

Trace each sample and write a row of each on notebook paper. Make all letters slant in the same direction.

ccc   or   orange   door   word

Copy each verse twice on notebook paper.

Jesus said, "I am the bread of life." — *John 6:35*

God told Joshua, "I will not fail thee, nor forsake thee." — *Joshua 1:5*

Penmanship Mastery I • Lesson 36
Note: *L 37 is a Journal Entry and copying Spelling List 7.*

Trace each sample and write a row of each on notebook paper.

lll   we   west   wet   tweet

Using your best penmanship, copy this verse 3 times.

All we like sheep have gone astray; we have turned every one to his own way.

—*Isaiah 53:6*

Lesson 38 • *Penmanship Mastery I*
Note: *L 39 is a test. See p. 124.*

30

Trace each sample and write a row of each on notebook paper.

Put each sports word on the base (1st, 2nd, 3rd, Home [4]) which matches the number of syllables it contains. If you get them all correct, you're a real sport! On notebook paper, list each base as the heading for four different columns of words.

baseball, basketball, coach, cross country, football, golf, mountain climbing, soccer, table tennis, track and field, volleyball

31

Trace each sample and write a row of each on notebook paper.

lll   *oi*   *toil*   *foil*

Copy each verse twice. Be sure to use your best penmanship.

Rejoice in the Lord alway: and again I say, Rejoice. —*Philippians 4:4*

Zion heard, and was glad; and the daughters of Judah rejoiced because of thy judgments, O Lord. —*Psalm 97:8*

A WORD to Live by

Dependability

Jesus Christ the same yesterday, and to day, and for ever.

Hebrews 13:8

"A dependable person can be trusted to do what he is supposed to do—even when no one else is watching." Think about this. Copy the quotation on notebook paper, and then write what you think the quotation means.

Copy Spelling List 8.

33

Trace each sample and write a row of each on notebook paper.

Ul ba ba bag batter

Copy this sentence 3 times on notebook paper.

The Bahamas is a group of islands that attracts many tourists.

We can always depend on God to meet our needs.
We can always depend on Him to do what He says He will do.
What are some things God promises us?

PROGRESS
REPORT

Work on:

	Excellent	Very Good	Good	Fair	Poor
Letters with Tails					
Formation					
Uniform Slant					

Lesson 43 • *Penmanship Mastery I*
Note: *L 44 is a test. See p. 125.*

34

Warm Up

Trace each sample and write a row of each on notebook paper.

m m m

Practice

Draw and address an envelope correctly, using the following name and address. Write your return address in the upper left-hand corner. Design your own stamp.

Miss Lisa Scott
8 Rowe Hill Road
Waldo, Maine 04910

Practice

Copy the first stanza of "Hiawatha's Childhood" from your spelling book. Follow the poetry format for each line.

Trace each sample and write a row of each on notebook paper.

ccc   oa oa   board   coat

Copy this sentence twice, filling in the missing word.

An ___ tree produces acorns.

Copy this quotation twice.

Study the Bible to be wise, believe it to be safe, practice it to be holy.

Trace each sample and write a row of each on notebook paper.

ccc   ci   city   circle

Copy this quotation carefully 3 times.
Then write what it means to you.

Whatever makes men good Christians makes them good citizens. —*Daniel Webster*

37

Penmanship Mastery I • Lesson 48
Note: *L 49 is a test. See p. 125.*

Warm Up

Trace each sample and write a row of each on notebook paper.

Practice

Rewrite this thank-you note, adding all the missing punctuation and capital letters.

Dear aunt josie

thank you for inviting me for dinner yesterday. I always have fun at your house Thank you for making chocolate pie too. I hope that I will see you again soon

love
Chris

Trace each sample and write a row of each on notebook paper.
Watch your ending strokes on all letters.

ll *bo* *boat* *bottle*

Copy this poem twice.

Always Finish

If a task is once begun,
Never leave it till it's done.
Be the labor great or small,
Do it well or not at all.

39

A WORD to Live by

Whoso trusteth in the LORD, happy is he.

Proverbs 16:20

Read the example and then write some of your own definitions of happiness on notebook paper. Use your imagination and sense of humor:

Happiness is having covers to duck under when you're scared at night.

Thought Question: What brings the only happiness that will never leave us? Answer in complete sentences.

Copy Spelling List 10.

Trace each sample and write a row of each on notebook paper.

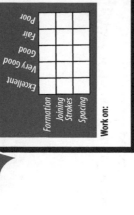

ee   br   bread   brother

abroad

Copy this poem carefully 2 times.

All things bright and beautiful,
All creatures great and small,
All things wise and wonderful,
The Lord God made them all.

Penmanship Mastery I • Lesson 53
Note: *L 54 is a test. See p. 125.*

Trace each sample and write a row of each on notebook paper:

Can you "state" these abbreviations? Copy state names onto notebook paper and write the abbreviation beside it. Use careful penmanship!

1. Alabama	9. Florida
2. West Virginia	10. Georgia
3. Arizona	11. Wyoming
4. Arkansas	12. Vermont
5. California	13. Illinois
6. Colorado	14. Indiana
7. Connecticut	15. Wisconsin
8. Delaware	

VT	WV	WY
CA	IN	WI
DE	FL	
GA	CT	
IL	AR	
AL	AZ	
CO		

Trace each sample and write a row of each on notebook paper. Watch your joining strokes.

ccc   od   God   code   dodge

Copy this prayer twice.

Thank You, God, for this nice day,
Thank You for my work and play;
For Your care the whole day through.
Thank You, God, For all You do.
　　　　　Amen.

Penmanship Mastery I • Lesson 56

Note: L 57 is a Journal Entry and copying Spelling List 11.

43

Trace each sample and write a row of each on notebook paper.

lll os os hose close

Copy the verse carefully 2 times.

Give, and it shall be given unto you; good measure, pressed down, and shaken together, and running over, shall men give into your bosom. For with the same measure that ye mete withal it shall be measured to you again. *—Luke 6:38*

PROGRESS REPORT

Work on:

	Excellent	Very Good	Good	Fair	Poor
Formation					
Joining					
Strokes					
Spacing					

Lesson 58 • *Penmanship Mastery I*
Note: *L 59 is a test. See p.125.*

44

Trace each sample and write a row of each on notebook paper.

ccc

Compound words are made up of two separate words written together.

Example: honey + bee = honeybee

How many compound words can you you make from these words? Write your answers on notebook paper. (Use each word only once.) Then use each word in a sentence.

police	light	head	ground
sail	man	rain	lights
over	boat	rail	bow
moon	coat	play	road

45

Trace each sample and write a row of each on notebook paper.

eee   h   he   hetter   Bethel

Bethlehem   robe

Copy each sentence carefully 2 times.

Ellen bought a beautiful silver bell.

When I do my best, my penmanship is better.

Beavers live beside the stream.

A WORD to Live by

Greatness

Great is the Lord, and greatly to be praised; and His greatness is unsearchable.

Psalm 145:3

 What are some qualities which make a person great? Write them in complete sentences on notebook paper.

 Write about a person that you think is a truly great person. Why is he or she great?

 Copy Spelling List 12.

Lesson 63 • *Penmanship Mastery I*
Note: *L 64 is a test. See p. 126.*

48

Warm Up

Trace each sample and write a row of each on notebook paper.

ccc   go   goal   gone

Practice

Copy each quotation carefully 3 times.

The foundation of our government is first, that every man shall govern himself. —*Abbott*

'Tis the good reader that makes the good book.
　　　　　　　　　　　　　　　—*Emerson*

He who waits to do a great deal of good at once will never do anything. —*Johnson*

Trace the sample and write a row on notebook paper.

You can do a fun trick with your 9 times tables. (a) Under the 9, write backwards to 0. (b) Under the 0, write forward to 9. When you are finished, you will have written the answers for your 9 times table! (c) Fill in the missing numbers to complete your 9 times table. (d) Copy the table a second time being careful to slant each number.

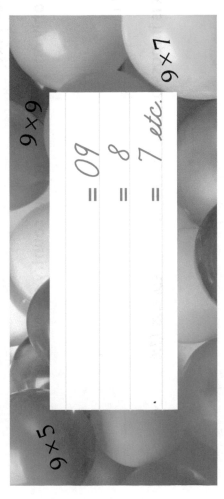

9×9

9×5

= 09

= 8

= 7 etc.

9×7

49

Trace each sample and write a row of each on notebook paper. Check that loops are properly formed.

Ull fa false fair fashion

Carefully copy this quotation twice.

I regret that I have only one life to lose for my country. —*Nathan Hale*

Carefully copy this verse 3 times.

But without faith it is impossible to please Him. —*Hebrews 11:6*

PROGRESS REPORT

Lowercase Formation	Excellent	Very Good	Good	Fair	Poor
Loops					
Ovals					
Humps					

Work on:

Trace each sample and write a row of each on notebook paper.

ttt   og   Roger   log

Copy each sentence 3 times using your best penmanship.

Hot dogs are good with mustard.

I like to jump on a pogo stick.

Pongo's doghouse is too small for him.

Penmanship Mastery I • Lesson 68

Note: L 69 is a test. See p. 126.

51

Trace each sample and write a row of each on notebook paper.

eee

Do you know the names for the babies of each animal in the list? Copy each animal name, and write the baby animal's name that matches its mother. If you get stumped, choose from the list below. Write your list 2 times.

1. *kangaroo*   6. *sheep*

2. *mare*   7. *frog*

3. *deer*   8. *goose*

4. *cow*   9. *duck*

5. *bear*   10. *pig*

foal, fawn, lamb, piglet, joey, tadpole, calf, cub, gosling, duckling

Trace each sample and write a row of each on notebook paper. Retrace correctly as you form letters.

ccc   oh   ohoh   Johnson   John

Copy this poem twice.

Oh where, oh where has my little dog gone?
Oh where, oh where can he be?
With his tail cut short and his ears cut long,
Oh where, oh where can he be?

A WORD to Live by

Whatsoever thy hand findeth to do, do it with thy might.

Ecclesiastes 9:10

Effort

What are some things you could do better if you tried harder?

Copy this prayer.

**Let me do the thing that ought to be done,
when it ought to be done,
as it ought to be done,
whether I like to do it or not.**

Copy Spelling List 14.

Trace each sample and write a row of each on notebook paper.

ui   wh   whale   white

Carefully copy these quotations 3 times each.

**The God who gave us life
gave us liberty at the same time.** *—Thomas Jefferson*

Where liberty dwells, there is my country. *—Benjamin Franklin*

Penmanship Mastery I • Lesson 73

55

Note: *L 74 is a test. See p. 126.*

© 2008–2015 Educational Ventures, Inc. Not to be reproduced.

Trace each sample and write a row of each on notebook paper.

lelele

Pretend that you are away at summer camp. Write a note to your parents telling them what you are doing.

Trace each sample and write a row of each on notebook paper. Dot and cross letters correctly.

ulll *ba* *be* *bi* *bo* *bu*

bitter *Bill*

Copy this paragraph about the Bible 2 times.

Everybody ought to read the Bible. Everybody. It is God's Word. It holds the solution of life. It tells about the best Friend mankind ever had, the noblest, kindest, truest Man that ever trod this earth. —*Henry Halley*

Penmanship Mastery I • Lesson 76
Note: *L 77 is a Journal Entry and copying Spelling List 15.*

Trace each sample and write a row of each on notebook paper.

lll   tt   little   letter

Copy this poem 2 times carefully.

Betty Botter bought some butter,
But she said, "The butter's bitter;
If I put it in my batter
It will make my batter bitter,
But a bit of better butter,
That would make my batter better."

Lesson 78 • *Penmanship Mastery I*
Note: *L 79 is a test. See p. 126.*

58

PROGRESS REPORT

Work on:

	Excellent	Very Good	Good	Fair	Poor
Lowercase Formation					
Retraced Letters					
Dotted and Crossed Letters					
Letters with Tails					

Trace each sample and write a row of each on notebook paper.

Copy the state abbreviations onto notebook paper. Write the name of the state beside its abbreviation. Write list 2 times.

1. NH

2. NJ

3. NM

4. NY

5. NC

6. ND

7. TN

8. OK

9. OR

10. PA

11. RI

12. SC

Trace each sample and write a row of each on notebook paper.

th jo jot joy Jonathan

Copy this quotation 3 times. Write carefully.

Good company in a journey makes the way seem shorter. *—Izaak Walton*

Contentment

A WORD to Live by

Not that I speak in respect of want: for I have learned, in whatsoever state I am, therewith to be content.

Philippians 4:11

Copy the Bible verse about contentment. Use your best penmanship.

The Apostle Paul wrote the Bible verse which you just copied. He was in prison when he wrote it. What do you think he meant about learning to be content no matter where he was?

Copy Spelling List 16.

Trace each sample and write a row of each on notebook paper.

All All Bless blood Blend

Copy these verses in your best penmanship.

Bless the Lord, O my soul: and all that is within me, bless His holy name. Bless the Lord, O my soul, and forget not all His benefits. —*Psalm 103:1–2*

How can you be content today at school?

Lesson 83 • *Penmanship Mastery I*
Note: *L 84 is a test. See p. 127.*

62

Warm Up

Trace each sample and write a row of each on notebook paper.

ccc

Practice

A prefix is a syllable which comes in front of a word and changes its meaning. Combine the following prefixes and root words to make new words. Write each one three times. Then use each word in the left column in a good sentence.

ab + normal =	anti + freeze =
ad + verb =	post + pone =
tri + cycle =	mis + treat =
un + happy =	in + correct =
re + trace =	post + script =
sub + marine =	un + even =

63

Trace each sample and write a row of each on notebook paper. Check your formation.

ccc   os od os og oh   ob   awoke   joke

Copy this paragraph.

The Okefenokee Swamp extends from southern Georgia into northern Florida. You might see alligators, water moccasins, otters, raccoons, and deer there. There are about 50 different kinds of fish living there. It would be a great place to visit.

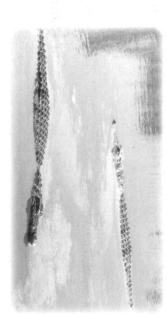

Lesson 86 • Penmanship Mastery I
Note: L 87 is a Journal Entry and copying Spelling List 17.

64

Trace each sample and write a row of each on notebook paper.

lll   on   pond   don't   one

Using your best penmanship, copy these quotations 3 times each.

Listening is fifty percent of our education.

Honesty is the best policy.

Well begun is half done.

PROGRESS REPORT

	Excellent	Very Good	Good	Fair	Poor
Formation					
Proportion					
Spacing					

Work on:

Penmanship Mastery I • Lesson 88
Note: *L 89 is a test. See p. 127.*

65

© 2008–2015 Educational Ventures, Inc. Not to be reproduced.

Trace each sample and write a row of each on notebook paper.

elelel

Copy the paragraph and finish by adding 2 or more sentences of your own.

I knocked, but no one answered. Slowly, I pushed the door and it slid open. The lights were all on, but I could hear nothing. I stepped inside....

Trace each sample and write a row of each on notebook paper. Check for correct proportions in your writing.

mmm   onom   broom   home   Mom

Copy the verses. Be careful to use correct spacing.

And this is His commandment, That we should believe on the name of His Son Jesus Christ, and love one another, as He gave us commandment. *—1 John 3:23*

If any of you lack wisdom, let him ask of God, that giveth to all men liberally, and upbraideth not; and it shall be given him. *—James 1:5*

A WORD to Live by

Wisdom

Happy is the man that findeth wisdom, and the man that getteth understanding.

Proverbs 3:13

Using your best penmanship, copy these Bible verses about wisdom 2 times each.

Happy is the man that findeth wisdom, and the man that getteth understanding. —*Proverbs 3:13*

How much better is it to get wisdom than gold! and to get understanding rather to be chosen than silver! —*Proverbs 16:16*

Copy Spelling List 18.

Trace each sample and write a row of each on notebook paper.

Hf of opera popcorn

Copy this poem. Watch carefully for capitalization and punctuation.

As to the Restless Brook

Do you suppose the babbling brook
Would stop and rest its head
If someone got a scoop and took
The pebbles from its bed?

—*John Kendrick Bangs*

Penmanship Mastery I • Lesson 93
Note: L 94 is a test. See p. 127.

Trace the sample and write a row on notebook paper.

How many words can you find in this circle?
You may not skip over letters, and all your
words must contain three letters or more.
Use each of the first 5 words in sentences.

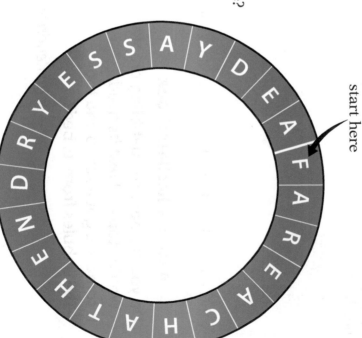

start here

Trace each sample and write a row of each on notebook paper. Check to see that letters are resting on lines.

ccc   ot   otter   motor   knot

Carefully copy this poem 2 times.

Others, Lord, yes others,
Let this my motto be,
Help me to live for others
That I may live like Thee.

—Meigs

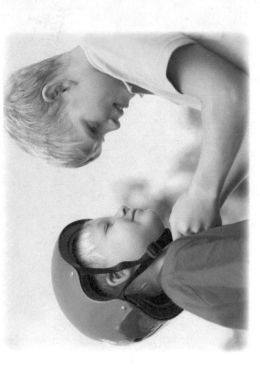

Penmanship Mastery I • Lesson 96

Note: L 97 is a Journal Entry and copying Spelling List 19.

71

Warm Up

Trace each sample and write a row of each on notebook paper.

ccc oc doctor lock sock

Practice

Copy each sentence 2 times each carefully.

An octopus has eight arms.

The game of hockey began in Canada.

Independence Day is a special occasion.

PROGRESS REPORT

Work on:

	Excellent	Very Good	Good	Fair	Poor
Formation					
Proportion					
Spacing					

Lesson 98 • Penmanship Mastery I

Note: L 99 is a test. See p. 128.

72

Warm Up

Trace each sample and write a row of each on notebook paper.

eeeee

Practice

How many words can you make? Combine a prefix with a root word in the same column. Write a row of each new word.

Prefix	Root Word	Prefix	Root Word	Prefix	Root Word
con	vantage	re	port	un	cover
anti	form	mis	merge	bi	obey
ad	freeze	post	spell	pro	cycle
ex	view	sub	phone	dis	duce
inter	ist	trans	trace		

Penmanship Mastery I • Lesson 100

Trace each sample and write a row of each on notebook paper.

ououou oa oi ou mouse around could

Using your best penmanship, copy this quotation and verse 2 times each.

Time lost is never found again.

Humble yourselves therefore
under the mighty hand of God,
that He may exalt you in due time.
—1 Peter 5:6

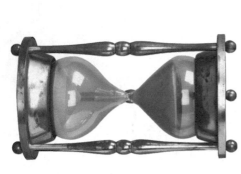

A WORD to Live by

Thoughtfulness

And as ye would that men should do to you, do ye also to them likewise.

Luke 6:31

 Think of thoughtful things that you could do this week for the following people. Write your ideas in complete sentences.

your mom, your dad, your teacher, your pastor, your best friend, a classmate

 Copy Spelling List 20.

Trace each sample and write a row of each on notebook paper:

uu uu buffalo sunburn hamburger

Copy these sentences carefully.

Buddy brought a bundle of wood for the fire.

I brought hamburgers and hot dogs to roast.

Copy this quotation.

Life is short but there is always time for courtesy. —*Emerson*

Lesson 103 • *Penmanship Mastery I*

Note: *L 104 is a test. See p. 128.*

76

PROGRESS REPORT

Work on:

	Excellent	Very Good	Good	Fair	Poor
Formation					
Proportion					
Spacing					

Trace each sample and write a row of each on notebook paper.

elelel

Copy the following animal names three times. Use each of the first five in a good sentence.

baboon	buffalo	deer	donkey	elephant
giraffe	horse	lamb	moose	owl
rabbit	sheep	tarantula	walrus	wolf

77

Trace each sample and write a row of each on notebook paper.
Check your circles and upward strokes in the formation of your letters.

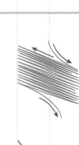

vrvrvr   vri   vrictory   vrivrid   vrillage

divide   advise

Copy this poem 2 times. Include all punctuation.

Patience is a virtue,
  Virtue is a grace;
Both put together
  Make a very pretty face.

Warm Up

Trace each sample and write a row of each on notebook paper.

seee   ro   volunteer   vote

avoid

Practice

Copy each sentence 3 times.

Iwo Jima is a volcanic island in the Pacific Ocean.

Volleyball is a popular sport in America.

© 2008–2015 Educational Ventures, Inc. Not to be reproduced.

79

Penmanship Mastery I • Lesson 108
Note: *L 109 is a test. See p. 128.*

Trace each sample and write a row of each on notebook paper.

Read the clue, then write an answer which begins with the letter *s*.

1. person who takes care of sheep
2. found on the beach
3. day after Saturday
4. high tower on a church
5. put on an envelope before mailing
6. a green, leafy vegetable
7. opposite of deep
8. boat made to go underwater
9. a group of words that expresses a complete thought
10. sprinkled on food for flavor

Trace each sample and write a row of each on notebook paper. Check that loops are made correctly.

weee ou our towel bowl

owl flower town

Copy this quotation carefully 2 times.

All wish to possess knowledge, but few are willing to pay the price.

Write some things you could do to cheer up someone who is sad.

81

A WORD to Live by

Cheerfulness

A merry heart maketh a cheerful countenance.

Proverbs 15:13

Discuss this quotation with your teacher and classmates. Then, in your own words, write what you think it means.

The world is a looking glass and gives back to every man the reflection of his own face.

—William Makepeace Thackeray

Copy Spelling List 22.

Warm Up

Trace each sample and write a row of each on notebook paper.

ccc   ox   fox   boxer

chicken pox   White sox

Practice

Copy this verse carefully 3 times.

Where no oxen are, the crib is clean: but much increase is by the strength of the ox. —*Proverbs 14:4*

Penmanship Mastery I • Lesson 113

Note: *L 114 is a test. See p. 128.*

83

Trace each sample and write a row of each on notebook paper.

The clue letter is *k*! Can you decode the following? On notebook paper, write the clue word with the answer beside it.

Begins with Clue

1. ruler of a country
2. a young cat
3. Australian animal
4. unlocks doors
5. room for cooking

Clue within Word

1. fun place to swim
2. what we eat at Thanksgiving
3. worn outside when it's cool
4. to grasp onto something
5. something fun to tell and listen to

Ends with Clue

1. inside a pen
2. to search for something is to
3. to pull tight quickly
4. to say something
5. color lighter than red

If you get stumped, here are some clues: **turkey, jerk, ink, lake, king, look, joke, speak, take, jacket, kitchen, key, pink, kangaroo, kitten**

Trace each sample and write a row of each on notebook paper.

ccc   oy   Joy   toys   oyster

Copy this verse 2 times carefully. Be sure to use your best penmanship.

O come, let us sing unto the Lord:
let us make a joyful noise to the rock
of our salvation. *—Psalm 95:1*

Trace each sample and write a row of each on notebook paper.

Ht   Oy   Ozz   doze

Copy each sentence 2 times.

The farmer's wife gathered three dozen eggs

before sunrise.

The ozone is a layer of condensed oxygen

that surrounds the earth.

Lesson 118 • Penmanship Mastery I

Note: L 119 is a test. See p. 129.

86

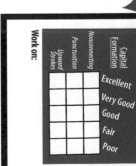

PROGRESS REPORT

Work on:

	Excellent	Very Good	Good	Fair	Poor
Capital Formation					
Nonconnecting Punctuation					
Upward Strokes					

Trace each sample and write a row of each on notebook paper.

m m m

List the words under the correct headings: Computer Words / Calendar Words.
List each word 3 times.

December   **Wednesday**

Tuesday

monitor   **program**

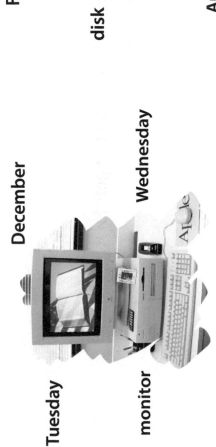

February   **keyboard**

disk

August   **mouse**

Penmanship Mastery I • Lesson 120

Trace each sample and write a row of each on notebook paper.
Check that loops are the right size.

lll   lly   bye-bye   baby   ruby

Copy this quotation 3 times.

**The highest reward for man's toil is not what he gets for it
but what he becomes by it.**   —*John Ruskin*

Patience

For ye have need of patience, that, after ye have done the will of God, ye might receive the promise.

Hebrews 10:36

Using your best penmanship, copy the Bible verse about patience two times.

Copy Spelling List 24.

Trace each sample and write a row of each on notebook paper.

Using your best penmanship, copy the Bible verses.

O offer unto God thanksgiving. -Psalm 50:14

Whoso offereth praise glorifieth me.
-Psalm 50:23

A patient person bears pains or trials or opposition without complaining. Write about someone you know who is patient.

Lesson 123 • *Penmanship Mastery I*
Note: *L 124 is a test. See p. 129.*

90

PROGRESS REPORT

Work on:

	Excellent	Very Good	Good	Fair	Poor
Capital Formation					
Nonconnecting					
Punctuation					
Upward Strokes					

Trace each sample and write a row of each on notebook paper.

Write a note to the President letting him know that you are praying for him. Be specific about what you are including in your prayers.

Trace each sample and write a row of each on notebook paper.

ccc oa oi ou oo look troop spoon

Copy this poem 2 times.

An Oyster from Kalamazoo

An oyster from Kalamazoo,
Confessed he was feeling quite blue.
"For," said he, "as a rule,
When the weather turns cool,
I'm apt to get into a stew."

Trace each sample and write a row of each on notebook paper.

uu   *ad*   *shade*   *ladder*

Copy each sentence 2 times.

John Quincy Adams was the sixth President of the United States.

Adoniram Judson was an American missionary to Burma.

PROGRESS REPORT

	Excellent	Very Good	Good	Fair	Poor
Capital Formation					
Upward Strokes					
Loops					
Nonconnecting					

Work on:

Penmanship Mastery I • Lesson 128

Note: *L 129 is a test. See p. 129.*

93

Trace each sample and write a row of each on notebook paper.

Write your address and the President's address 2 times each on notebook paper.

President
1600 Pennsylvania Avenue, N.W.
Washington, D.C. 20500

Trace each sample and write a row of each on notebook paper. Practice connecting capital letters correctly.

ucucuc   *Qu*   *Quaber*   *Queen Victoria*

Quiz 2

Copy this verse carefully 2 times.

He hath showed thee, O man, what is good; and what doth the Lord require of thee, but to do justly, and to love mercy, and to walk humbly with thy God?   —*Micah 6:8*

A WORD to Live by

And ye shall know the truth, and the truth shall make you free.

John 8:32

Freedom

Discuss this question with your teacher and then write the answer in your own words.

Why do you think there are more freedoms in America than there are in many other countries? How did we get those freedoms?

Copy Spelling List 26.

PROGRESS REPORT

Lowercase Formation	Excellent	Very Good	Good	Fair	Poor
Joining Strokes					
Ending Strokes					
Upward Strokes					

Work on:

Trace each sample and write a row of each on notebook paper.

ll wa walk wave away

Practice

Copy each sentence carefully 2 times.

George Washington Carver discovered more than 300 uses for the peanut.

The Pacific Ocean is the largest body of water in the world.

Penmanship Mastery I • Lesson 133
Note: *L 134 is a test. See p. 129.*

Trace each sample and write a row of each on notebook paper.

WANTED:

Sharp student to list following words under correct headings:
Birds / Metals

blue jay	bronze	aluminum	mercury
copper	falcon	quail	nickel
silver	tin	iron	robin
eagle	brass	cardinal	whippoorwill
gold	hawk	partridge	woodpecker

Trace each sample and write a row of each on notebook paper.

Ill ob job cobbler Bob obedience

Copy this verse 3 times.

Children, obey your parents in all things:
for this is well pleasing unto the Lord. —*Colossians 3:20*

Penmanship Mastery I • Lesson 136
Note: L 137 is a Journal Entry and copying Spelling List 27.

Trace each sample and write a row of each on notebook paper.

clclcl   fo   follow   football

Using your best penmanship, copy the Bible verses 2 times each.

Then said Jesus, Father, forgive them;
for they know not what they do. —*Luke 23:34*

And be not conformed to this world: but be ye
transformed by the renewing of your mind. —*Romans 12:2*

PROGRESS REPORT

Work on:

	Excellent	Very Good	Good	Fair	Poor
Capital Formation					
Upward Strokes					
Loops					
Nonconnecting					

Trace each sample and write a row of each on notebook paper.

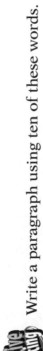

ccc

Write a paragraph using ten of these words.

school	car	phone
tree	milk	run
before	cow	two
friend	cookie	now
horn	white	yesterday

Penmanship Mastery I • Lesson 140

Trace each sample and write a row of each on notebook paper. Check your upward strokes.

All to at trolley dollar hold

Copy these quotations carefully 2 times each.

A Christian scholar will do all his schoolwork to the glory of God.

Honesty is not only the first step toward greatness, it is greatness itself.

Patriotism

A WORD to Live by

Put them in mind to be subject to principalities and powers, to obey magistrates, to be ready to every good work.

Titus 3:1

Using your best penmanship, copy the Bible verse 2 times.

Copy Spelling List 28.

Penmanship Mastery I • Lesson 142

Trace each sample and write a row of each on notebook paper:

uuuuu   aa ae ai ao au

Ca Ce Ci Co Cu   L L L L

Tuesday   September

Copy each sentence carefully 2 times.

Students should listen closely to their teachers.

The best way to have friends is to be a friend.

What comes to your mind when you hear the word *patriotism?* Write the words on notebook paper:

the flag

Lesson 143 • Penmanship Mastery I
Note: L 144 is a test. See p. 130.

104

Trace each sample and write a row of each on notebook paper.

Write a question on notebook paper for each of the answers given below. Then copy the answer on the line under your question.

A: Brazil is in South America.

A: The Nile River is 4,160 miles long.

A: Rome is the capital of Italy.

A: The highest mountain in the world is Mount Everest.

A: Tokyo is Japan's most important city.

Trace each sample and write a row of each on notebook paper.
Make your loops carefully.

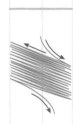

Ill   Ure   would   work   wonder   wood

Copy this fun poem carefully 2 times.

A sparrow sat on a window sill
And shook his head in doubt.
He wondered where those bookworms were
He'd heard so much about!

	Excellent	Very Good	Good	Fair	Poor
Capital Formation					
Upward Strokes					
Loops					
Nonconnecting					

Work on:

Trace each sample and write a row of each on notebook paper.

wi   William   wind

whippoorwill

Copy this verse 2 times.

**Have not I commanded thee? Be strong and of a good courage;
be not afraid, neither be thou dismayed: for the Lord thy God
is with thee whithersoever thou goest.   —Joshua 1:9**

Penmanship Mastery I • Lesson 148
Note: *L 149 is a test. See p. 130.*

107

Trace each sample and write a row of each on notebook paper:

Write each definition and then write the history or science term that matches.
The terms are listed below. Be sure to spell correctly.

1. an unsettled, empty land

2. a large, southern, colonial farm

3. the study of the universe

4. the study of the earth's surface

5. animals with backbones

6. a ruler who allows no freedom

7. the scientific study of the ocean

8. to look carefully at something

9. any form of water that falls from the clouds

10. free from another person's or country's control

11. the force that draws things toward the earth

12. the story of what has happened
in the life of a country or people

*independent, wilderness, vertebrates, gravity, observe, oceanography, dictator, science, precipitation,
plantation, history, geography*

Trace each sample and write a row of each on notebook paper.

ll   wr   write   wrinkle   wren

wrong   wrapped

Copy this verse 2 times using your best penmanship.

**But he that doeth wrong shall receive for the wrong which he hath done;
and there is no respect of persons.** —*Colossians 3:25*

A WORD to Live by

Charity

And above all these things put on charity, which is the bond of perfectness.

Colossians 3:14

A good synonym for charity is love.

Using your best penmanship, carefully copy this verse about charity 2 times.

And now abideth faith, hope, charity, these three; but the greatest of these is charity.

—*1 Corinthians 13:13*

Copy Spelling List 30.

Trace each sample and write a row of each on notebook paper.

ccc   oe   does   goes   toe

Copy each sentence 2 times.

I am wearing my new shoes.

Dad asked Joe to hoe the garden.

The Bible says that charity (love) is a great attribute. Why do you think this is true? In your own words write what you think "true charity" is.

Penmanship Mastery I • Lesson 153

Note: *L 154 is a test. See p. 131.*

wwww

Synonyms are words of the same or nearly the same meaning.
Can you match the following synonyms? Write your answers on notebook paper.

1.	sea	midday
2.	noon	error
3.	artist	sad
4.	mistake	blaze
5.	utensil	fog
6.	unhappy	ocean
7.	thankful	painter
8.	mist	tool
9.	flame	grateful

Trace each sample and write a row of each on notebook paper.

ee   ed   Ed   editor   painted

Copy this poem carefully 2 times on notebook paper.

Grape Marmalade

There once was a clever young maid
Who only ate grape marmalade.
At one hundred and three
She said with a *WHEE!*
"How nicely preserved I have stayed!"

Penmanship Mastery I • Lesson 156

Note: *L 157 is a Journal Entry and copying Spelling List 31.*

Trace each sample and write a row of each on notebook paper.

ccc   or   cover   love   oval

Copy each sentence 3 times.

Isaac Newton discovered gravity in 1687.

Christopher Columbus discovered America in 1492.

Lesson 158 • Penmanship Mastery I

Note: L 159 is a test. See p. 131.

114

Trace each sample and write a row of each on notebook paper.

Antonyms are words with opposite meanings.
Can you match the following antonyms?
Write your answers on notebook paper.

1. worthless
2. cowardly
3. slowly
4. stingy
5. rude
6. permanent
7. broad
8. defeat
9. careless
10. beginning

brave
conclusion
courteous
generous
narrow
rapidly
cautious
temporary
valuable
victory

tall, thin

short, fat

Penmanship Mastery I • Lesson 160

115

Trace each sample and write a row of each on notebook paper.
Check all letters for proper slant.

yt yo yogurt young youie your

Copy these quotations 2 times each.

**Success in your classes depends
upon your ability to finish the job.**

No rule of success will work if you don't.

A WORD to Live by

Kindness

And be ye kind one to another, tenderhearted, forgiving one another, even as God for Christ's sake hath forgiven you.

Ephesians 4:32

To speak kindly does not hurt the tongue.

Name some kind things that you can say when someone has been nice to you.

Question: If a classmate accidentally broke your pen, what would be the kind thing for you to do?

Copy Spelling List 32.

Warm Up

Trace each sample and write a row of each on notebook paper.

g g g   H H   Ha He Hi Ho Hu

Ha He Hi Ho Hu

 Practice

Copy each sentence twice on notebook paper.

Good students must work hard.

Happiness comes from the heart.

 Practice

Using your best penmanship, write this Bible verse.

**Because thy lovingkindness is better than life,
my lips shall praise thee.** —*Psalm 63:3*

Lesson 163 • *Penmanship Mastery I*
Note: *L 164 is a test. See p. 131.*

118

Work on:

	Excellent	Very Good	Good	Fair	Poor
Loops					
Slant					
Tails					

PROGRESS REPORT

Warm Up

Trace each sample and write a row of each on notebook paper.

Creative Writing

At the bottom of the page find an antonym which gives an opposite meaning of each numbered word and write each pair 3 times on notebook paper.

1. guilty	6. sharp
2. slow	7. empty
3. hard	8. young
4. remember	9. false
5. decrease	10. light

| 11. wet |
| 12. front |
| 13. poor |
| 14. late |
| 15. below |

increase	early	full
dark	easy	back
above	old	innocent
forget	rich	dull
true	fast	dry

119

Trace each sample and write a row of each on notebook paper.
Practice uniform spacing.

enemen   ve   velvet   envelope   ever

Copy each sentence 3 times.

Tomatoes are fruits, not vegetables.

Mom took the cat to the veterinarian.

PROGRESS REPORT

	Excellent	Very Good	Good	Fair	Poor
Formation					
Proportion					
Spacing					

Work on:

 Trace each sample and write a row of each on notebook paper.

nnn   ng   long

wrong   singing

 Copy this song 2 times.

A Home on the Range

Home, home on the range,
Where the deer and the antelope play;
Where seldom is heard a discouraging word
And the skies are not cloudy all day.

Penmanship Mastery I • Lesson 168
Note: *L 169 is a test. See p. 131.*

121

Trace each sample and write a row of each on notebook paper.

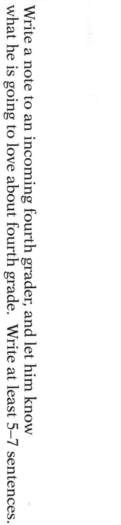

Write a note to an incoming fourth grader, and let him know what he is going to love about fourth grade. Write at least 5–7 sentences.

Penmanship Tests

Trial Test
Lesson 4

Time to Rise

A birdie with a yellow bill
Hopped upon the window sill,
Cocked his shining eye and said:
"Ain't you 'shamed, you sleepy-head!"

—*Robert Louis Stevenson*

Test 1
Lesson 9

The Owl

A wise old owl sat in an oak.
The more he heard, the less he spoke.
The less he spoke, the more he heard.
Why aren't we all like that wise old bird?

—*Christina Rossetti*

Test 2
Lesson 14

Isaiah 53:1–3

Who hath believed our report? and to whom is the arm of the Lord revealed? For He shall grow up before him as a tender plant, and as a root out of a dry ground: He hath no form nor comeliness; and when we shall see Him, there is no beauty that we should desire Him. He is despised and rejected of men; a man of sorrows, and acquainted with grief: and we hid as it were our faces from Him; He was despised, and we esteemed Him not.

Test 3
Lesson 19

A Nation's Strength

Not gold, but only man can make
    A people great and strong;
Men who, for truth and honor's sake,
    Stand fast and suffer long.

Brave men who work while others sleep.
    Who dare while others fly—
They build a nation's pillars deep
    And lift them to the sky.

—*Ralph Waldo Emerson*

123

Penmanship Mastery I • Tests

Test 4
Lesson 24

Isaiah 53:4-6

Surely He hath borne our griefs, and carried our sorrows: yet we did esteem Him stricken, smitten of God, and afflicted. But He was wounded for our transgressions, He was bruised for our iniquities: the chastisement of our peace was upon Him; and with His stripes we are healed. All we like sheep have gone astray; we have turned every one to his own way; and the Lord hath laid on Him the iniquity of us all.

Test 5
Lesson 29

Declaration of Independence

We hold these truths to be self-evident:—that all men are created equal; that they are endowed by their Creator with certain unalienable rights; that among these are life, liberty, and the pursuit of happiness; that, to secure these rights, governments are instituted among men, deriving their just powers from the consent of the governed.

Test 6
Lesson 34

America the Beautiful

O beautiful for spacious skies,
  For amber waves of grain,
For purple mountain majesties
  Above the fruited plain!
America! America!
  God shed His grace on thee,
And crown thy good with brotherhood
  From sea to shining sea.

—*Katharine Lee Bates*

Test 7
Lesson 39

Books of the Old Testament

Genesis	2 Chronicles	Daniel
Exodus	Ezra	Hosea
Leviticus	Nehemiah	Joel
Numbers	Esther	Amos
Deuteronomy	Job	Obadiah
Joshua	Psalms	Jonah
Judges	Proverbs	Micah
Ruth	Ecclesiastes	Nahum
1 Samuel	Song of Solomon	Habakkuk
2 Samuel	Isaiah	Zephaniah
1 Kings	Jeremiah	Haggai
2 Kings	Lamentations	Zechariah
1 Chronicles	Ezekiel	Malachi

124

Test 8
Lesson 44

Psalm 1:1-3

Blessed is the man that walketh not in the counsel of the ungodly, nor standeth in the way of sinners, nor sitteth in the seat of the scornful. But his delight is in the law of the Lord; and in His law doth he meditate day and night. And he shall be like a tree planted by the rivers of water, that bringeth forth his fruit in his season; his leaf also shall not wither; and whatsoever he doeth shall prosper.

Test 9
Lesson 49

Books of the New Testament

Matthew	Ephesians	Hebrews
Mark	Philippians	James
Luke	Colossians	1 Peter
John	1 Thessalonians	2 Peter
Acts	2 Thessalonians	1 John
Romans	1 Timothy	2 John
1 Corinthians	2 Timothy	3 John
2 Corinthians	Titus	Jude
Galatians	Philemon	Revelation

Test 10
Lesson 54

Work

I am glad a task to me is given
To labor day by day;
For it brings me health, and strength, and hope,
And I cheerfully learn to say,
"Head, you may think; Heart, you may feel,
But Hand, you should work always."

—*Louisa M. Alcott*

Test 11
Lesson 59

We Gather Together

We gather together to ask the Lord's blessing,
He chastens and hastens His will to make known;
The wicked oppressing now cease from distressing:
Sing praises to His name, He forgets not His own.

125

Isaiah 53:7–9

He was oppressed, and He was afflicted,
yet He opened not His mouth: He is brought
as a lamb to the slaughter, and as a sheep
before her shearers is dumb, so He openeth
not His mouth. He was taken from prison
and from judgment: and who shall declare
His generation? for He was cut off out of the
land of the living: for the transgression of my
people was He stricken. And He made His
grave with the wicked, and with the rich in
His death; because He had done no violence,
neither was any deceit in His mouth.

Building Eternity

Little drops of water,
   Little grains of sand
Make the mighty ocean
   And the pleasant land.

Thus the little minutes
   Humble though they be,
Make the mighty ages
   Of eternity.

—*Ebenezer Cobham Brewer*

Luke 2:8–11

And there were in the same country shep-
herds abiding in the field, keeping watch over
their flock by night. And, lo, the angel of the
Lord came upon them, and the glory of the
Lord shone round about them: and they were
sore afraid. And the angel said unto them,
Fear not: for, behold, I bring you good tidings
of great joy, which shall be to all people. For
unto you is born this day in the city of David a
Savior, which is Christ the Lord.

Don't Give Up

If you've tried and have not won,
   Never stop for crying;
All that's great and good is done
   Just by patient trying.

If by easy work you beat,
   Who the more will prize you?
Gaining victory from defeat,
   That's the test that tries you.

—*Phoebe Cary*

Stately Verse

If Mary goes far out to sea,
By wayward breezes fanned,
I'd like to know—can you tell me?—
Just where would Maryland?

If Tenny went high up in air
And looked o'er land and sea,
Looked here and there and everywhere,
Pray what would Tennessee?

I looked out of the window and
Saw Orry on the lawn;
He's not there now, and who can tell
Just where has Oregon?

Two girls were quarreling one day
With garden tools, and so
I said, "My dears, let Mary rake
And just let Idaho."

An English lady had a steed.
She called him 'Ighland Bay.
She rode for exercise, and thus
Rhode Island every day.

Matthew 5:3–8

Blessed are the poor in spirit: for theirs is the kingdom of heaven. Blessed are they that mourn: for they shall be comforted. Blessed are the meek: for they shall inherit the earth. Blessed are they which do hunger and thirst after righteousness: for they shall be filled. Blessed are the merciful: for they shall obtain mercy. Blessed are the pure in heart: for they shall see God.

Matthew 5:9–12

Blessed are the peacemakers: for they shall be called the children of God. Blessed are they which are persecuted for righteousness' sake: for theirs is the kingdom of heaven. Blessed are ye, when men shall revile you, and persecute you, and shall say all manner of evil against you falsely, for my sake. Rejoice, and be exceeding glad: for great is your reward in heaven: for so persecuted they the prophets which were before you.

Test 19
Lesson 99

My Country, 'Tis of Thee

My country, 'tis of thee,
Sweet land of liberty,
Of thee I sing:
Land where my fathers died,
Land of the pilgrims' pride,
From ev'ry mountain side
Let freedom ring!

Our fathers' God, to thee,
Author of liberty,
To thee we sing:
Long may our land be bright
With freedom's holy light;
Protect us by thy might,
Great God, our King!

—*Samuel Francis Smith*

Test 20
Lesson 104

Psalm 100

Make a joyful noise unto the Lord, all ye lands. Serve the Lord with gladness: come before His presence with singing. Know ye that the Lord He is God: it is He that hath made us, and not we ourselves; we are His people, and the sheep of His pasture. Enter into His gates with thanksgiving, and into His courts with praise: be thankful unto Him, and bless His name. For the Lord is good; His mercy is everlasting; and His truth endureth to all generations.

Test 21
Lesson 109

The Flea and the Fly

A flea and a fly got caught in a flue.
   Said the fly, "Let us flee."
   Said the flea, "Let us fly."
So together they flew through a flaw in the flue.

Test 22
Lesson 114

Proverbs 1:7-10

The fear of the Lord is the beginning of knowledge: but fools despise wisdom and instruction. My son, hear the instruction of thy father, and forsake not the law of thy mother: For they shall be an ornament of grace unto thy head, and chains about thy neck. My son, if sinners entice thee, consent thou not.

A Bird

A bird came down the walk:
He did not know I saw;
He bit an angleworm in halves
And ate the fellow, raw.

And then he drank a dew
From a convenient grass,
And then hopped sidewise to the wall
To let a beetle pass.

—*Emily Dickinson*

Isaiah 40:28–31

Hast thou not known? hast thou not heard, that the everlasting God, the Lord, the Creator of the ends of the earth, fainteth not, neither is weary? there is no searching of His understanding. He giveth power to the faint; and to them that have no might He increaseth strength. Even the youths shall faint and be weary, and the young men shall utterly fall: But they that wait upon the Lord shall renew their strength; they shall mount up with wings as eagles; they shall run, and not be weary; and they shall walk, and not faint.

My Responsibility

I am glad to think
I am not bound to make the world go right,
But only to discover and to do,
With cheerful heart, the work that God
appoints.

I will trust in Him,
That He can hold His own; and I will take
His will, above the work He sendeth me,
To be my chiefest good. The glory is not in
the task,
But in the doing it for Him.

—*Jean Ingelow*

Song of Solomon 2:11–13

For, lo, the winter is past, the rain is over and gone; The flowers appear on the earth; the time of the singing of birds is come, and the voice of the turtle is heard in our land; The fig tree putteth forth her green figs, and the vines with the tender grape give a good smell.

Lincoln's Gettysburg Address
(excerpt)

Fourscore and seven years ago our fathers brought forth upon this continent a new nation, conceived in liberty, and dedicated to the proposition that all men are created equal.

Now we are engaged in a great civil war, testing whether that nation, or any nation so conceived and so dedicated, can long endure.

Matthew 22:36–40

Master, which is the great commandment in the law? Jesus said unto him, Thou shalt love the Lord thy God with all thy heart, and with all thy soul, and with all thy mind. This is the first and great commandment. And the second is like unto it, Thou shalt love thy neighbor as thyself. On these two commandments hang all the law and the prophets.

Rain in Summer

How beautiful is the rain!
After the dust and heat,
In the broad and fiery street,
In the narrow lane,
How beautiful is the rain!

How it clatters along the roofs,
Like the tramp of hoofs!
How it gushes and struggles out
From the throat of the overflowing spout!

Across the window pane
It pours and pours;
And swift and wide,
With a muddy tide,
Like a river down the gutter roars
The rain, the welcome rain!

In the country, on every side,
Where far and wide,
Like a leopard's tawny and spotted hide,
Stretches the plain,
To the dry grass and the drier grain
How welcome is the rain!

—Henry Wadsworth Longfellow

1 Thessalonians 4:16-18

For the Lord Himself shall descend from heaven with a shout, with the voice of the archangel, and with the trump of God: and the dead in Christ shall rise first: Then we which are alive and remain shall be caught up together with them in the clouds, to meet the Lord in the air: and so shall we ever be with the Lord. Wherefore comfort one another with these words.

The Star-Spangled Banner

O say! can you see, by the dawn's early light,
What so proudly we hailed at the twilight's
	last gleaming,
Whose broad stripes and bright stars, through
	the perilous fight
O'er the ramparts we watch'd, were so gal-
	lantly streaming?
And the rockets' red glare, the bombs bursting
	in air,
Gave proof through the night that our flag
	was still there.
O say, does that star-spangled banner yet wave
O'er the land of the free and the home of the
	brave?

The Grasshopper and the Elephant

Way down south where bananas grow,
	A grasshopper stepped on an elephant's toe,
The elephant said, with tears in his eyes,
	"Pick on somebody your own size."

John 16:7-11

Nevertheless I tell you the truth; It is expedient for you that I go away: for if I go not away, the Comforter will not come unto you; but if I depart, I will send Him unto you. And when He is come, He will reprove the world of sin, and of righteousness, and of judgment: Of sin, because they believe not on Me; Of righteousness, because I go to My Father, and ye see Me no more; Of judgment, because the prince of this world is judged.

Slant Guide